Top Pup
and
Bad Rat

D1637575

Maverick
Early Readers

'Top Pup' and 'Bad Rat'
An original concept by Katie Dale
© Katie Dale

Illustrated by Giusi Capizzi

Published by MAVERICK ARTS PUBLISHING LTD
Studio 11, City Business Centre, 6 Brighton Road,
Horsham, West Sussex, RH13 5BB
© Maverick Arts Publishing Limited August 2021
+44 (0)1403 256941

A CIP catalogue record for this book is available at the British Library.

ISBN 978-1-84886-811-3

www.maverickbooks.co.uk

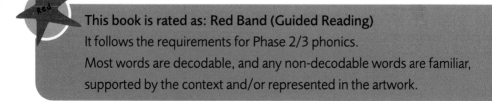

This book is rated as: Red Band (Guided Reading)
It follows the requirements for Phase 2/3 phonics.
Most words are decodable, and any non-decodable words are familiar,
supported by the context and/or represented in the artwork.

Top Pup
and
Bad Rat

By **Katie Dale**
Illustrated by **Giusi Capizzi**

The Letter T

Trace the lower and upper case letter with a finger. Sound out the letter.

Down,
lift,
cross

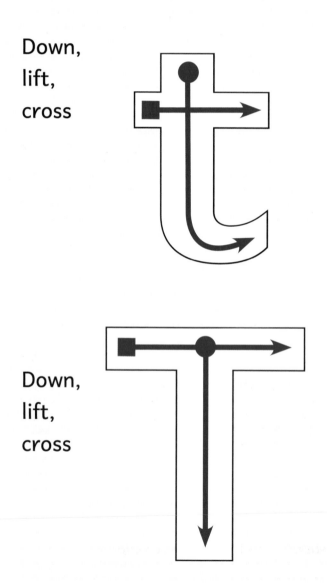

Down,
lift,
cross

Some words to familiarise:

kitten   duck   chick

High-frequency words:

I   to   me   the   no   we

Tips for Reading 'Top Pup'

- Practise the words listed above before reading the story.

- If the reader struggles with any of the other words, ask them to look for sounds they know in the word. Encourage them to sound out the words and help them read the words if necessary.

- After reading the story, ask the reader how everyone helped Fox.

Fun Activity

Pretend you're a superhero! Who will you help?

Top Pup

Top Pup zooms to the sad kitten.

Top Pup zooms to the sad duck.

I can help!

Top Pup zooms to the sad chick.

12

The Letter R

Trace the lower and upper case letter with a finger. Sound out the letter.

Down,
up,
around

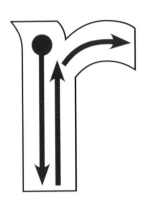

Down,
up,
around,
down

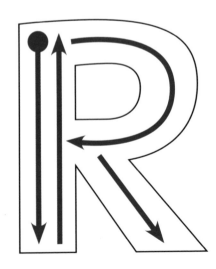

Some words to familiarise:

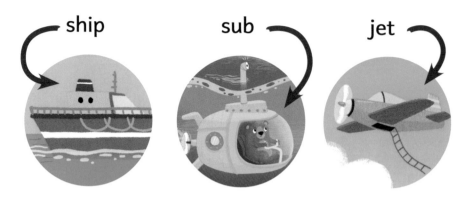

ship   sub   jet

High-frequency words:

a   of   I   has   on   him   we

Tips for Reading 'Bad Rat'

- Practise the words listed above before reading the story.

- If the reader struggles with any of the other words, ask them to look for sounds they know in the word. Encourage them to sound out the words and help them read the words if necessary.

- After reading the story, ask the reader why everyone wanted to get Bad Rat.

Fun Activity

Discuss what could happen next in the story.

Bad Rat nicks a bag of buns!

Hen has a van. But...

But...

But…

...Bad Rat gets on a jet!

I cannot get him!

Book Bands for Guided Reading

Pink
Red
Yellow
Blue
Green
Orange
Turquoise
Purple
Gold
White

The Institute of Education book banding system is a scale of colours that reflects the various levels of reading difficulty. The bands are assigned by taking into account the content, the language style, the layout and phonics. Word, phrase and sentence level work is also taken into consideration.

Maverick Early Readers are a bright, attractive range of books covering the pink to white bands. All of these books have been book banded for guided reading to the industry standard and edited by a leading educational consultant.

To view the whole Maverick Readers scheme, visit our website at www.maverickearlyreaders.com

Or scan the QR code above to view our scheme instantly!